STEPHEN JAY GOULD

ADAM'S NAVEL
AND OTHER ESSAYS

PENGUIN BOOKS

PENGUIN BOOKS

Published by the Penguin Group. Penguin Books Ltd, 27 Wrights Lane, London w8 5TZ, England. Penguin Books USA Inc., 375 Hudson Street, New York, New York 10014, USA. Penguin Books Australia Ltd, Ringwood, Victoria, Australia. Penguin Books Canada Ltd, 10 Alcorn Avenue, Toronto, Ontario, Canada M4V 3B2. Penguin Books (NZ) Ltd, 182–190 Wairau Road, Auckland 10, New Zealand · Penguin Books Ltd, Registered Offices: Harmondsworth, Middlesex, England · **These extracts are taken from *The Flamingo's Smile, Bully for Brontosaurus* and *Eight Little Piggies*, published by Penguin Books in 1987, 1992 and 1994 respectively.** This edition published 1995 · All rights reserved. Copyright © Stephen Jay Gould, 1985, 1991, 1993 · The moral right of the author has been asserted · Typeset by Datix International Limited, Bungay, Suffolk. Printed in England by Clays Ltd, St Ives plc · Except in the United States of America, this book is sold subject to the condition that it shall not, by way of trade or otherwise, be lent, re-sold, hired out, or otherwise circulated without the publisher's prior consent in any form of binding or cover other than that in which it is published and without a similar condition including this condition being imposed on the subsequent purchaser · 10 9 8 7 6 5 4 3 2 1

CONTENTS

Adam's Navel

The ample fig leaf served our artistic forefathers well as a botanical shield against indecent exposure for Adam and Eve, our naked parents in the primeval bliss and innocence of Eden. Yet, in many ancient paintings, foliage hides more than Adam's genitalia; a wandering vine covers his navel as well. If modesty enjoined the genital shroud, a very different motive – mystery – placed a plant over his belly. In a theological debate more portentous than the old argument about angels on pinpoints, many earnest people of faith had wondered whether Adam had a navel.

He was, after all, not born of a woman and required no remnant of his nonexistent umbilical cord. Yet, in creating a prototype, would not God make his first man like all the rest to follow? Would God, in other words, not create with the appearance of pre-existence? In the absence of definite guidance to resolve this vexatious issue, and not wishing to incur anyone's wrath, many painters literally hedged and covered Adam's belly.

A few centuries later, as the nascent science of geology gathered evidence for the earth's enormous antiquity, some advocates of biblical literalism revived this old argument for our entire planet. The strata and their entombed fossils surely seem to represent a sequential record of countless years, but wouldn't God create his earth with the appearance of pre-existence? Why should we not believe that he created strata and fossils to give modern life a harmonious order by granting it a sensible (if illusory) past? As God provided Adam with a navel to stress continuity with future men, so too did he endow a pristine world with the appearance of an ordered history. Thus, the earth might be but a few thousand years old, as Genesis literally affirmed, and still record an apparent tale of untold eons.

This argument, so often cited as a premier example of reason at its most perfectly and preciously ridiculous, was most seriously and comprehensively set forth by the British naturalist Philip Henry Gosse in 1857. Gosse paid proper homage to historical context in choosing a title for his volume. He named it *Omphalos* (Greek for navel), in Adam's honor, and added as a subtitle: *An Attempt to Untie the Geological Knot.*

Since *Omphalos* is such spectacular nonsense, readers may rightly ask why I choose to discuss it at all. I do so, first of all, because its author was such a serious and fascinating man, not a hopeless crank or malcontent. Any honest passion merits our attention, if only for the oldest of stated reasons – Terence's celebrated *Homo sum: humani nihil a me alienum puto* (I am human, and am therefore indifferent to nothing done by humans).

Philip Henry Gosse (1810–88) was the David Attenborough of his day, Britain's finest popular narrator of nature's fascination. He wrote a dozen books on plants and animals, lectured widely to popular audiences, and published several technical papers on marine invertebrates. He was also, in an age given to strong religious feeling as a mode for expressing human passions denied vent elsewhere, an extreme and committed fundamentalist of the Plymouth Brethren sect. Although his *History of the British Sea-Anemones* and other assorted ramblings in natural history are no longer read, Gosse retains some notoriety as the elder figure in that classical work of late Victorian self-analysis and personal exposé, his son Edmund's wonderful account of a young boy's struggle against a crushing religious extremism imposed by a caring and beloved parent – *Father and Son*.

My second reason for considering *Omphalos* invokes the same theme surrounding so many of these essays about nature's small oddities: Exceptions do prove rules (prove, that is, in the sense of probe or test, not affirm). If you want to understand what ordinary folks do, one thoughtful deviant will teach you more than ten thousand solid citizens. When we grasp why *Omphalos* is so unacceptable (and not, by the way, for the reason usually cited), we will understand better how science and useful logic proceed. In any case, as an exercise in the anthropology of knowledge, *Omphalos* has no parallel – for its surpassing strangeness arose in the mind of a stolid Englishman, whose general character and cultural setting we can grasp as akin to our own, while the exotic systems of alien cultures are terra incognita both for their content and their context.

To understand *Omphalos*, we must begin with a paradox. The argument that strata and fossils were created all at once with the earth, and only present an illusion of elapsed time, might be easier to appreciate if its author had been an urban armchair theologian with no feeling or affection for nature's works. But how could a keen naturalist, who had spent days, nay months, on geological excursions, and who had studied fossils hour after hour, learning their distinctions and memorizing their names, possibly be content with the prospect that these objects of his devoted attention had never existed – were, indeed, a kind of grand joke perpetrated upon us by the Lord of All?

Philip Henry Gosse was the finest descriptive naturalist of his day. His son wrote: 'As a collector of facts and marshaller of observations, he had not a rival in that age.' The problem lies with the usual caricature of *Omphalos* as an argument that God, in fashioning the earth, had consciously and elaborately lied either to test our faith or simply to indulge in some inscrutable fit of arcane humor. Gosse, so fiercely committed both to his fossils and his God, advanced an opposing interpretation that commanded us to study geology with diligence and to respect all its facts even though they had no existence in real time. When we understand why a dedicated empiricist could embrace the argument of *Omphalos* ('creation with the appearance of pre-existence'), only then can we understand its deeper fallacies.

Gosse began his argument with a central, but dubious, premise: All natural processes, he declared, move endlessly round in a circle: egg to chicken to egg, oak to acorn to oak.

This, then, is the order of all organic nature. When once we are in any portion of the course, we find ourselves running in a circular groove, as endless as the course of a blind horse in a mill . . . [In pre-mechanized mills, horses wore blinders or, sad to say, were actually blinded, so that they would continue to walk a circular course and not attempt to move straight forward, as horses relying on visual cues tend to do.] This is not the law of some particular species, but of all: it pervades all classes of animals, all classes of plants, from the queenly palm down to the protococcus, from the monad up to man: the life of every organic being is whirling in a ceaseless circle, to which one knows not how to assign any commencement . . . The cow is as inevitable a sequence of the embryo, as the embryo is of the cow.

When God creates, and Gosse entertained not the slightest doubt that all species arose by divine fiat with no subsequent evolution, he must break (or 'erupt', as Gosse wrote) somewhere into this ideal circle. Wherever God enters the circle (or 'places his wafer of creation', as Gosse stated in metaphor), his initial product must bear traces of previous stages in the circle, even if these stages had no existence in real time. If God chooses to create humans as adults, their hair and nails (not to mention their navels) testify to previous growth that never occurred. Even if he decides to create us as a simple fertilized ovum, this initial form implies a phantom mother's womb and two non-existent parents to pass along the fruit of inheritance.

Creation can be nothing else than a series of irruptions into circles . . . Supposing the irruption to have been made at what part of the circle we please, and varying this condition indefinitely at will, – we cannot avoid the conclusion that each organism was from the first marked with the records of a previous being. But since creation and previous history are inconsistent with each other; as the very idea of the creation of an organism excludes the idea of pre-existence of that organism, or of any part of it; it follows, that such records are false, so far as they testify to time.

Gosse then invented a terminology to contrast the two parts of a circle before and after an act of creation. He labeled as 'prochronic', or occurring outside of time, those appearances of pre-existence actually fashioned by God at the moment of creation but seeming to mark earlier stages in the circle of life. Subsequent events occurring after creation, and unfolding in conventional time, he called 'diachronic'. Adam's navel was prochronic, the 930 years of his earthly life diachronic.

Gosse devoted more than 300 pages, some 90 per cent of his text, to a simple list of examples for the following small part of his complete argument – if species arise by sudden creation at any point in their life cycle, their initial form must present illusory (prochronic) appearances of pre-existence. Let me choose just one among his numerous illustrations, both to characterize his style of argument and to present his gloriously purple prose.

If God created vertebrates as adults, Gosse claimed, their teeth imply a prochronic past in patterns of wear and replacement.

Gosse leads us on an imaginary tour of life just an hour after its creation in the wilderness. He pauses at the seashore and scans the distant waves:

I see yonder a . . . terrific tyrant of the sea . . . It is the grisly shark. How stealthily he glides along . . . Let us go and look into his mouth . . . Is not this an awful array of knives and lancets? Is not this a case of surgical instruments enough to make you shudder? What would be the amputation of your leg to this row of triangular scalpels?

Yet the teeth grow in spirals, one behind the next, each waiting to take its turn as those in current use wear down and drop out:

It follows, therefore, that the teeth which we now see erect and threatening, are the successors of former ones that have passed away, and that they were once dormant like those we see behind them . . . Hence we are compelled by the phenomena to infer a long past existence to this animal, which yet has been called into being within an hour.

Should we try to argue that teeth in current use are the first members of their spiral, implying no predecessors after all, Gosse replies that their state of wear indicates a prochronic past. Should we propose that these initial teeth might be unmarred in a newly created shark, Gosse moves on to another example.

Away to a broader river. Here wallows and riots the huge hippopotamus. What can we make of his dentition?

All modern adult hippos possess strongly worn and beveled canines and incisors, a clear sign of active use throughout a long life. May we not, however, as for our shark, argue that a newly created hippo might have sharp and pristine front teeth? Gosse argues correctly that no hippo could work properly with teeth in such a state. A created adult hippo must contain worn teeth as witnesses of a prochronic past:

The polished surfaces of the teeth, worn away by mutual action, afford striking evidence of the lapse of time. Some one may possibly object . . . 'What right have you to assume that these teeth were worn away at the moment of its creation, admitting the animal to have been created adult. May they not have been entire?' I reply, Impossible: the Hippopotamus's teeth would have been perfectly useless to him, except in the ground-down condition: nay, the unworn canines would have effectually prevented his jaws from closing, necessitating the keeping of the mouth wide open until the attrition was performed; long before which, of course, he would have starved . . . The degree of attrition is merely a question of time . . . How distinct an evidence of past action, and yet, in the case of the created individual, how illusory!

This could go on forever (it nearly does in the book), but just one more dental example. Gosse, continuing upward on the topographic trajectory of his imaginary journey, reaches an inland wood and meets *Babirussa*, the famous Asian pig with upper canines growing out and arching back, almost piercing the skull:

In the thickets of this nutmeg grove beside us there is a Babiroussa; let us examine him. Here he is, almost submerged in this tepid pool. Gentle swine with the circular tusk, please to open your pretty mouth!

The pig, created by God but an hour ago, obliges, thus displaying his worn molars and, particularly, the arching canines themselves, a product of long and continuous growth.

I find this part of Gosse's argument quite satisfactory as a solution, within the boundaries of his assumptions, to that classical dilemma of reasoning (comparable in importance to angels on pinpoints and Adam's navel): 'Which came first, the chicken or the egg?' Gosse's answer: 'Either, at God's pleasure, with prochronic traces of the other.' But arguments are only as good as their premises, and Gosse's inspired nonsense fails because an alternative assumption, now accepted as undoubtedly correct, renders the question irrelevant – namely, evolution itself. Gosse's circles do not spin around eternally; each life cycle traces an ancestry back to inorganic chemicals in a primeval ocean. If organisms arose by acts of creation *ab nihilo*, then Gosse's argument about prochronic traces must be respected. But if organisms evolved to their current state, *Omphalos* collapses to massive irrelevance. Gosse understood this threat perfectly well and chose to meet it by abrupt dismissal. Evolution, he allowed, discredited his system, but only a fool could accept such patent nonsense and idolatry (Gosse wrote *Omphalos* two years before Darwin published the *Origin of Species*).

If any choose to maintain, as many do, that species were gradually brought to their present maturity from humbler forms . . . he is welcome to his hypothesis, but I have nothing to do with it. These pages will not touch him.

But Gosse then faced a second and larger difficulty: the prochronic argument may work for organisms and their life cycles, but how can it be applied to the entire earth and its fossil record – for Gosse intended *Omphalos* as a treatise to reconcile the earth with biblical chronology, 'an attempt to untie the geological knot'. His statements about prochronic parts in organisms are only meant as collateral support for the primary geological argument. And Gosse's geological claim fails precisely because it rests upon such dubious analogy with what he recognized

8

(since he gave it so much more space) as a much stronger argument about modern organisms.

Gosse tried valiantly to advance for the entire earth the same two premises that made his prochronic argument work for organisms. But an unwilling world rebelled against such forced reasoning and *Omphalos* collapsed under its own weight of illogic. Gosse first tried to argue that all geological processes, like organic life cycles, move in circles:

The problem, then, to be solved before we can certainly determine the question of analogy between the globe and the organism, is this – Is the life-history of the globe a cycle? If it is (and there are many reasons why this is probable), then I am sure prochronism must have been evident at its creation, since there is no point in a circle which does not imply previous points.

But Gosse could never document any inevitable geological cyclicity, and his argument drowned in a sea of rhetoric and biblical allusion from Ecclesiastes: 'All the rivers run into the sea; yet the sea *is* not full. Unto the place from whence the rivers come, thither they return again.'

Secondly, to make fossils prochronic, Gosse had to establish an analogy so riddled with holes that it would make the most ardent mental tester shudder – embryo is to adult as fossil is to modern organism. One might admit that chickens require previous eggs, but why should a modern reptile (especially for an anti-evolutionist like Gosse) be necessarily linked to a previous dinosaur as part of a cosmic cycle? A python surely does not imply the ineluctable entombment of an illusory *Triceratops* into prochronic strata.

With this epitome of Gosse's argument, we can resolve the paradox posed at the outset. Gosse could accept strata and fossils as illusory and still advocate their study because he did not regard

9

the prochronic part of a cycle as any less 'true' or informative than its conventional diachronic segment. God decreed two kinds of existence – one constructed all at once with the appearance of elapsed time, the other progressing sequentially. Both dovetail harmoniously to form uninterrupted circles that, in their order and majesty, give us insight into God's thoughts and plans.

The prochronic part is neither a joke nor a test of faith; it represents God's obedience to his own logic, given his decision to order creation in circles. As thoughts in God's mind, solidified in stone by creation *ab nihilo*, strata and fossils are just as true as if they recorded the products of conventional time. A geologist should study them with as much care and zeal, for we learn God's ways from both his prochronic and his diachronic objects. The geological time scale is no more meaningful as a yardstick than as a map of God's thoughts.

The acceptance of the principles presented in this volume . . . would not, in the least degree, affect the study of scientific geology. The character and order of the strata . . . the successive floras and faunas; and all the other phenomena, would be facts still. They would still be, as now, legitimate subjects of examination and inquiry . . . We might still speak of the inconceivably long duration of the processes in question, provided we understand ideal instead of actual time – that the duration was projected in the mind of God, and not really existent.

Thus, Gosse offered *Omphalos* to practicing scientists as a helpful resolution of potential religious conflicts, not a challenge to their procedures or the relevance of their information.

His son Edmund wrote of the great hopes that Gosse held for *Omphalos*:

Never was a book cast upon the waters with greater anticipations of success than was this curious, this obstinate, this fanatical volume. My father lived in a fever of suspense, waiting for the tremendous issue. This '*Omphalos*' of his, he thought, was to bring all the turmoil of scientific speculation to a close, fling geology into the arms of Scripture, and make the lion eat grass with the lamb.

Yet readers greeted *Omphalos* with disbelief, ridicule, or worse, stunned silence. Edmund Gosse continued:

He offered it, with a glowing gesture, to atheists and Christians alike. This was to be the universal panacea; this the system of intellectual therapeutics which could not but heal all the maladies of the age. But, alas! atheists and Christians alike looked at it and laughed, and threw it away.

Although Gosse reconciled himself to a God who would create such a minutely detailed, illusory past, this notion was anathema to most of his countrymen. The British are a practical, empirical people, 'a nation of shopkeepers' in Adam Smith's famous phrase; they tend to respect the facts of nature at face value and rarely favor the complex systems of non-obvious interpretation so popular in much of continental thought. Prochronism was simply too much to swallow. The Reverend Charles Kingsley, an intellectual leader of unquestionable devotion to both God and science, spoke for a consensus in stating that he could not 'give up the painful and slow conclusion of five and twenty years' study of geology, and believe that God has written on the rocks one enormous and superfluous lie'.

And so it has gone for the argument of *Omphalos* ever since. Gosse did not invent it, and a few creationists ever since have revived it from time to time. But it has never been welcome or popular because it violates our intuitive notion of divine benevolence as free of devious behavior – for while Gosse saw divine brilliance in the idea of prochronism, most people cannot shuck their seat-of-the-pants feeling that it smacks of plain old unfairness. Our modern American creationists reject it vehemently as imputing a dubious moral character to God and opt instead for the even more ridiculous notion that our miles of fossiliferous strata are all products of Noah's flood and can therefore be telescoped into the literal time scale of Genesis.

But what is so desperately wrong with *Omphalos*? Only this really (and perhaps paradoxically): that we can devise no way to find out whether it is wrong – or, for that matter, right. *Omphalos* is the classical example of an utterly untestable notion, for the world will look exactly the same in all its intricate detail whether fossils and strata are prochronic or products of an extended history. When we realize that *Omphalos* must be rejected for this methodological absurdity, not for any demonstrated factual inaccuracy, then we will understand science as a way of knowing, and *Omphalos* will serve its purpose as an intellectual foil or prod.

Science is a procedure for testing and rejecting hypotheses, not a compendium of certain knowledge. Claims that can be proved incorrect lie within its domain (as false statements to be sure, but as proposals that meet the primary methodological criterion of testability). But theories that cannot be tested in principle are not part of science. Science is doing, not clever cogitation; we reject *Omphalos* as useless, not wrong.

Gosse's deep error lay in his failure to appreciate this essential character of scientific reasoning. He hammered his own coffin nails by continually emphasizing that *Omphalos* made no practical difference – that the world would look exactly the same with a prochronic or diachronic past. (Gosse thought that this admission would make his argument acceptable to conventional geologists; he never realized that it could only lead them to reject his entire scheme as irrelevant.) 'I do not know,' he wrote, 'that a single conclusion, now accepted, would need to be given up, except that of actual chronology.'

Gosse emphasized that we cannot know where God placed his wafer of creation into the cosmic circle because prochronic objects, created *ab nihilo*, look exactly like diachronic products of actual time. To those who argued that coprolites (fossil excrement) prove the existence of active, feeding animals in a real geological past, Gosse replied that as God would create adults with feces in their intestines, so too would he place petrified turds into his created strata. (I am not making up this example for comic effect; you will find it on page 353 of *Omphalos*.) Thus, with these words, Gosse sealed his fate and placed himself outside the pale of science:

Now, again I repeat, there is no imaginable difference to sense between the prochronic and the diachronic development. Every argument by which the physiologist can prove to demonstration that yonder cow was once a foetus in the uterus of its dam, will apply with exactly the same power to show that the newly created cow was an embryo, some years before its creation ... There is, and can be, nothing in the phenomena to indicate a commencement there, any more than anywhere else, or indeed, anywhere at all. The commencement, as a fact, I must learn from testimony; I have no means whatever of inferring it from phenomena.

Gosse was emotionally crushed by the failure of *Omphalos*. During the long winter evenings of his discontent, in the January cold of 1858, he sat by the fire with his eight-year-old son, trying to ward off bitter thoughts by discussing the grisly details of past and current murders. Young Edmund heard of Mrs Manning, who buried her victim in quicklime and was hanged in black satin; of Burke and Hare, the Scottish ghouls; and of the 13 'carpetbag mystery', a sackful of neatly butchered human parts hung from a pier on Waterloo Bridge. This may not have been the most appropriate subject for an impressionable lad (Edmund was, by his own memory, 'nearly frozen into stone with horror'), yet I take some comfort in the thought that Philip Henry Gosse, smitten with the pain of rejection for his untestable theory, could take refuge in something so unambiguously factual, so utterly concrete.

POSTSCRIPT

I have since learned that one of my favorite writers, Jorge Luis Borges, wrote a fascinating short comment on *Omphalos* ('The creation and P. H. Gosse' in *Other Inquisitions, 1937–1952*, published in 1964 by the University of Texas Press, Ruth L. C. Simms, translator). Borges begins by citing several literary references to the absence of a navel in our primal parents. Sir Thomas Browne, as a metaphor for original sin, writes in *Religio Medici* (1642), 'the man without a navel yet lives in me'; and James Joyce, in the first chapter of *Ulysses* (what cannot be found in this incredible book!) states, 'Heva, naked Eve. She had no navel.' I particularly appreciated the lovely epitome and insight of Borges's conclusion (though I disagree with his second point), 'I should like to emphasize two virtues in Gosse's forgotten thesis. First, its rather monstrous elegance. Second: its involuntary reduction of a *creatio ab nihilo* to absurdity, its indirect demonstration that the universe is eternal, as the Vedanta, Heraclitus, Spinoza and the atomists thought.'

The Median isn't the Message

My life has recently intersected, in a most personal way, two of Mark Twain's famous quips. One I shall defer to the end of this essay. The other (sometimes attributed to Disraeli) identifies three species of mendacity, each worse than the one before – lies, damned lies, and statistics.

Consider the standard example of stretching truth with numbers – a case quite relevant to my story. Statistics recognizes different measures of an 'average', or central, tendency. The *mean* represents our usual concept of an overall average – add up the items and divide them by the number of sharers (100 candy bars collected for five kids next Hallowe'en will yield 20 for each in a fair world). The *median*, a different measure of central tendency, is the halfway point. If I line up five kids by height, the median child is shorter than two and taller than the other two (who might have trouble getting their mean share of the candy). A politician in power might say with pride, 'The mean income of our citizens is $15,000 per year.' The leader of the opposition might retort, 'But half our citizens make less than $10,000 per year.' Both are right, but neither cites a statistic with impassive objectivity. The first invokes a mean, the second a median. (Means are higher than medians in such cases because one millionaire may outweigh hundreds of poor people in setting a mean, but can balance only one mendicant in calculating a median.)

The larger issue that creates a common distrust or contempt for statistics is more troubling. Many people make an unfortunate and invalid separation between heart and mind, or feeling and intellect. In some contemporary traditions, abetted by attitudes stereotypically centered upon Southern California, feelings are exalted as more 'real' and the only proper basis for action, while intellect gets short shrift as a hang-up of outmoded elitism. Statistics, in this absurd dichotomy, often becomes the symbol of the enemy. As Hilaire Belloc wrote, 'Statistics are the triumph of the quantitative method, and the quantitative method is the victory of sterility and death.'

This is a personal story of statistics, properly interpreted, as profoundly nurturant and life-giving. It declares holy war on the downgrading of intellect by telling a small story to illustrate the utility of dry, academic knowledge about science. Heart and head are focal points of one body, one personality.

In July 1982, I learned that I was suffering from abdominal mesothelioma, a rare and serious cancer usually associated with exposure to asbestos. When I revived after surgery, I asked my first question of my doctor and chemotherapist: 'What is the best technical literature about mesothelioma?' She replied, with a touch of diplomacy (the only departure she has ever made from direct frankness), that the medical literature contained nothing really worth reading.

Of course, trying to keep an intellectual away from literature works about as well as recommending chastity to *Homo sapiens*, the sexiest primate of all. As soon as I could walk, I made a bee-line for Harvard's Countway medical library and punched meso-thelioma into the computer's bibliographic search program. An hour later, surrounded by the latest literature on abdominal mesothelioma, I realized with a gulp why my doctor had offered that humane advice. The literature couldn't have been more brutally clear: mesothelioma is incurable, with a median mortality of only eight months after discovery. I sat stunned for about fifteen minutes, then smiled and said to myself: so that's why they didn't give me anything to read. Then my mind started to work again, thank goodness.

If a little learning could ever be a dangerous thing, I had encountered a classic example. Attitude clearly matters in fighting cancer. We don't know why (from my old-style materialistic perspective, I suspect that mental states feed back upon the immune system). But match people with the same cancer for age, class, health, and socioeconomic status, and, in general, those with positive attitudes, with a strong will and purpose for living, with commitment to struggle, and with an active response to aiding their own treatment and not just a passive acceptance of anything doctors say, tend to live longer. A few months later I asked Sir Peter Medawar, my personal scientific guru and a Nobelist in immunology what the best prescription for success against cancer might be. 'A sanguine personality,' he replied. Fortunately (since one can't reconstruct oneself at short notice and for a definite purpose), I am, if anything, even-tempered and confident in just this manner.

Hence the dilemma for humane doctors: since attitude matters so critically, should such a somber conclusion be advertised, especially since few people have sufficient understanding of statistics to evaluate what the statements really mean? From years of experience with the small-scale evolution of Bahamian land snails treated quantitatively, I have developed this technical knowledge – and I am convinced that it played a major role in saving my life. Knowledge is indeed power, as Francis Bacon proclaimed.

The problem may be briefly stated: what does 'median mortality of eight months' signify in our vernacular? I suspect that most people, without training in statistics, would read such a statement as 'I will probably be dead in eight months' – the very conclusion that must be avoided, both because this formulation is false, and because attitude matters so much.

I was not, of course, overjoyed, but I didn't read the statement in this vernacular way either. My technical training enjoined a different perspective on 'eight months median mortality'. The point may seem subtle, but the consequences can be profound. Moreover, this perspective embodies the distinctive way of thinking in my own field of evolutionary biology and natural history.

We still carry the historical baggage of a Platonic heritage that seeks sharp essences and definite boundaries. (Thus we hope to find an unambiguous 'beginning of life' or 'definition of death', although nature often comes to us as irreducible continua.) This Platonic heritage, with its emphasis on clear distinctions and separated immutable entities, leads us to view statistical measures of central tendency wrongly, indeed opposite to the appropriate interpretation in our actual world of variation, shadings, and continua. In short, we view means and medians as hard 'realities', and the variation that permits their calculation as a set of transient and imperfect measurements of this hidden essence. If the median is the reality and variation around the median just a device for calculation, then 'I will probably be dead in eight months' may pass as a reasonable interpretation.

But all evolutionary biologists know that variation itself is nature's only irreducible essence. Variation is the hard reality, not a set of imperfect measures for a central tendency. Means and medians are the abstractions. Therefore, I looked at the mesothelioma statistics quite differently – and not only because I am an optimist who tends to see the doughnut instead of the

18

hole, but primarily because I know that variation itself is the reality. I had to place myself amidst the variation.

When I learned about the eight-month median, my first intellectual reaction was: fine, half the people will live longer; now what are my chances of being in that half. I read for a furious and nervous hour and concluded, with relief: damned good. I possessed every one of the characteristics conferring a probability of longer life: I was young; my disease had been recognized in a relatively early stage; I would receive the nation's best medical treatment; I had the world to live for; I knew how to read the data properly and not despair.

Another technical point then added even more solace. I immediately recognized that the distribution of variation about the eight-month median would almost surely be what statisticians call 'right-skewed'. (In a symmetrical distribution, the profile of variation to the left of the central tendency is a mirror image of variation to the right. Skewed distributions are asymmetrical, with variation stretching out more in one direction than the other – left-skewed if extended to the left, right-skewed if stretched out to the right.) The distribution of variation had to be right-skewed, I reasoned. After all, the left of the distribution contains an irrevocable lower boundary of zero (since mesothelioma can only be identified at death or before). Thus, little space exists for the distribution's lower (or left) half – it must be scrunched up between zero and eight months. But the upper (or right) half can extend out for years and years, even if nobody ultimately survives. The distribution must be right-skewed, and I needed to know how long the extended tail ran – for I had already concluded that my favorable profile made me a good candidate for the right half of the curve.

The distribution was, indeed, strongly right-skewed, with a 19 long tail (however small) that extended for several years above the eight-month median. I saw no reason why I shouldn't be in that small tail, and I breathed a very long sigh of relief. My technical knowledge had helped. I had read the graph correctly. I had asked the right question and found the answers. I had obtained, in all probability, that most precious of all possible gifts in the circumstances – substantial time. I didn't have to stop and immediately follow Isaiah's injunction to Hezekiah – set thine house in order: for thou shalt die, and not live. I would have time to think, to plan, and to fight.

One final point about statistical distributions. They apply only to a prescribed set of circumstances – in this case to survival with mesothelioma under conventional modes of treatment. If circumstances change, the distribution may alter. I was placed on an experimental protocol of treatment and, if fortune holds, will be in the first cohort of a new distribution with high median and a right tail extending to death by natural causes at advanced old age.*

It has become, in my view, a bit too trendy to regard the acceptance of death as something tantamount to intrinsic dignity. Of course I agree with the preacher of Ecclesiastes that there is a time to love and a time to die – and when my skein runs out I hope to face the end calmly and in my own way. For most situations, however, I prefer the more martial view that death is the ultimate enemy – and I find nothing reproachable in those who rage mightily against the dying of the light.

The swords of battle are numerous, and none more effective than humor. My death was announced at a meeting of my colleagues in Scotland, and I almost experienced the delicious

* So far so good.

pleasure of reading my obituary penned by one of my best friends (the so-and-so got suspicious and checked; he too is a statistician, and didn't expect to find me so far out on the left tail). Still, the incident provided my first good laugh after the diagnosis. Just think, I almost got to repeat Mark Twain's most famous line of all: the reports of my death are greatly exaggerated.*

* Since writing this, my death has actually been reported in two European magazines, five years apart. *Fama volat* (and lasts a long time). I squawked very loudly both times and demanded a retraction; guess I just don't have Mr Clemens's *savoir faire*.

Unenchanted Evening

Tahiti is the stereotype, virtually the synonym, of enchantment in our legends. Nurse Forbush from Little Rock might have been a charmer (especially when played by Mary Martin), but the South Sea locale made a strong contribution to 'some enchanted evening'. (And Ezio Pinza, that greatest of operatic Don Giovannis, slumming on Broadway, didn't hurt the scene either.)

Some aspects of the legend need correction. Point Venus, for example, still the landing spot for many tourists, is not named for the beauty of Tahiti's women, but for astronomy and Captain Cook, who set up his instruments at the site to measure the transit of the planet Venus across the disk of the sun in 1769. Charles Darwin himself was beguiled both by the name and the place when he arrived on the *Beagle* in November 1835:

We landed to enjoy all the delights of the first impressions produced by a new country, and that country the charming Tahiti. A crowd of men, women and children, was collected on the memorable point Venus, ready to receive us with laughing, merry faces.

Darwin, however, broke ranks with male convention in expressing a lack of enthusiasm for Tahiti's women: 'I was much disappointed in the personal appearance of the women; they are far inferior in every respect to the men.' He objected most of all to the current fad in coiffure:

An unbecoming fashion in one respect is now almost universal: it is the cutting of hair, or rather shaving it, from the upper part of the head, in a circular form, so as to leave only an outer ring of hair. The missionaries have tried to persuade the people to change this habit: but it is the fashion, and that is sufficient answer at Tahiti as well as at Paris.

Darwin's heterodox judgment had not been widely shared. Captain Bligh, who got such a bum rap from Charles Laughton, may not win any medals for grasping human psychology, but he was a great seaman and no more dictatorial than the normal run of British shipmasters. The celebrated mutiny on his *Bounty* owed as much to Fletcher Christian's longing for Tahiti and the woman he left behind as to any of Bligh's shipboard policies.

Tahiti may be beautiful, but the title for 'picture-perfect paradise' has usually been awarded – and rightly so in my judgment (for I have just returned from my first visit to French Polynesia) – to the neighboring island of Moorea. Located just twelve miles northwest of Tahiti, Moorea is an extinct volcano, with a soaring crater rim, deeply dissected by later erosion into jagged peaks and draperies. Seen from Tahiti, especially when enshrouded by its usual entourage of seemingly personal clouds, Moorea becomes a most fitting symbol of beauty combined with mystery. One day on Tahiti, Charles Darwin scaled a local peak and received his dose of Moorea's spell:

From the point which I attained, there was a good view of the distant island of Eimeo [the old name for Moorea] . . . On the lofty and broken pinnacles, white massive clouds were piled up, which formed an island in the blue sky, as Eimeo itself did in the blue ocean.

This impression of beauty and mystery has certainly persisted. Oscar Hammerstein used Moorea as his model for Bali Ha'i, the off-limits paradise of delight in *South Pacific:*

Bali Ha'i will whisper
On the wind of the sea:
'Here am I, your special Island
Come to me, come to me!'

Who could resist these enticements, especially for a few francs and a forty-minute ferry ride? So my son Ethan and I visited Moorea on our recent trip. We were not disappointed. Unfortunately, the lure of Bali Ha'i has attracted other guests, some not so harmless. This essay is a story of genocide in paradise, a preventable wholesale slaughter, just completed in one human generation. You do not know the tale only because it pitted snail against snail, rather than man against man. But do not breathe a sigh of relief for moral exculpation of our species. Snails killed snails, but humans imported the agent of death – consciously and for decent motives, but with tragic and easily avoidable misperception.

Oceanic islands are our great natural laboratories of evolution, the source of so many ideas about organic change and of so many classical examples from finches on the Galápagos to flies on Hawaii. The combination of geographic isolation and difficult access, with frequent absence of predators or competitors, provides explosive possibilities for creatures who manage to reach these bounteous havens. (On the Galápagos, for example, finches radiated into a series of ecological roles usually filled by several families of birds on continents. Some species eat seeds of varying sizes; others act like woodpeckers; one species uses cactus needles to pry insects out of crevices. Darwin was bamboozled during his celebrated visit and classified these birds into several groups. He only learned the true story and significance when a professional ornithologist surveyed his collection in London and recognized the anatomical signature of finches beneath all the diversity.)

Land snails provide some of our finest and most intensely studied examples – and for obvious reasons. Few manage to make the long and fortuitous ocean voyage (by such odd means of transport as natural rafts, mud on birds' feet, or hurricanes if the distances are not too great). The lucky immigrants often find an open world divided into numerous separate pieces (the islands of a chain), each available for colonization and each the eventual source of an evolutionary radiation. Moreover, with their legendary lack of range and their hermaphroditic nature, small founding populations of snails (right down to the absolute minimum of one) can readily become the source of isolated colonies and, eventually, new species. One rat on an island is a transient memory (unless she is a pregnant female); one snail, any snail, may be the progenitor of a vast and changing population.

The high islands of the Pacific are the most promising places of all, for they combine maximal isolation with ecological diversity (the full range from seashore to volcanic mountain top). Many of these islands are formed by single and fairly symmetrical volcanoes. The volcano sides are often dissected into a series of radiating valleys from crater rim to sea. Since most land snails prefer moisture, they often live on the valley floors, but not on the intervening ridges. This common geography adds yet another ingredient to the evolutionary cauldron – a source of isolation within islands, as each valley becomes its own separate pocket. On the most diverse of oceanic islands, almost every valley may house a separate species of a particularly prolific snail.

The great radiations of Pacific island land snails are a glory of evolution and a source of joy and knowledge to those of us who have followed Darwin's footsteps into a profession. (I must confess to some jealousy here, for I have devoted my career to the less diverse land snails of low Atlantic islands – to *Poecilozonites* 25 on Bermuda, and *Cerion* on the Bahamas). Darwin's own Galápagos house a classic example – more than sixty endemic species of the family Bulimulidae. Even more famous (to cognoscenti, for I do not expect a general murmur of recognition here) are two great radiations on more isolated central Pacific islands – the several hundred species of Achatinellidae in the Hawaiian islands and the one hundred or so species of the genus *Partula* on Tahiti, Moorea, and their far-flung neighbors.

These high-island Pacific snails occupy an honored place in the history of evolutionary thought as foci for one of our great and extended debates. No animals seemed better suited for resolving a major issue about causes of organic change: what is the role of environment in evolution? In particular, do organisms change their form to fit altered conditions? And, if so, does environment work its influence directly by Lamarckian inheritance of characters acquired during life, or does form map environment through the indirect route of Darwinian adaptation by natural selection of the most fit in a random spectrum of variation?

Against these two different versions of adaptation – Lamarckian and Darwinian – other evolutionists asserted that form would not match environment in any clear way. The grossly maladapted will die, of course, but if variation arises only rarely and in definite directions, and if most alternatives are well enough suited to local environments, then adaptation will not shape the differences among populations. 'Internal causes' (direction of rare mutations), rather than external shaping (by natural selection), will then predominate in the production of evolutionary change.

What better test of these issues than the high-island Pacific snails? For if every valley housed a different population, think of the natural experiment thus provided. Many valleys would have nearly identical environments, but be colonized by only distantly related snails. If adaptation ruled, and climate shaped evolution in predictable ways, then the different snails of separate but similar valleys should evolve strong likenesses as adaptations to common conditions. But if 'internal factors' predominated, then no correlation of form and environment should be found among populations.

John T. Gulick (1832–1923), son of an American missionary who worked in Hawaii, fired the first important salvos in a series of works published between 1872 and 1905. Although Gulick spent most of his adult life as a missionary in China and Japan, he had, as a young man in his parents' parish, amassed an enormous collection of Hawaiian achatinellids. Gulick came down strongly for 'internal factors' and against control by natural selection or any other form of environmental influence. He could find no correlation between the forms of shells and the local environments of their valleys. Places with apparently identical vegetation, moisture, and temperature might harbor shells of maximally different form.

Gulick, who so strongly opposed (and primarily for religious reasons) the dominant determinism of the late nineteenth century, triumphantly concluded that the unpredictability of snail shells could be fully generalized to an overall defense of contingency in history, including human free will:

If my contention [that different forms arise in identical environments] is in accord with the facts, the assumption which we often meet that change in the organism is controlled in all its details by change in the environment, and that, therefore human progress is ruled by an external fate, is certainly contrary to fact. (From Gulick's famous 1905 treatise, *Evolution, Racial and Habitudinal.*)

When I first quoted this line in my Ph.D. thesis of 1969, I did so with derision (and as a firm adaptationist). Twenty years later, I am not so sure that Gulick was wrong in his implication. I still feel that his personal religious motive has no place in science, but people often reach correct answers for wrong or illogical reasons. The contingency of history (both for life in general and for the cultures of *Homo sapiens*) and human free will (in the factual rather than theological sense) are conjoined concepts, and no better evidence can be provided than the 'experimental' production of markedly different solutions in identical environments.

In any case, Gulick's conclusions drew a storm of protest from Darwinians. Alfred Russel Wallace, most committed of strict adaptationists, retorted (and not without justice) that Gulick's supposedly 'identical' environments might only seem so to humans, but would appear markedly different to snails:

It is an error to assume that what seem to us identical conditions are really identical to such small and delicate organisms as these land molluscs of whose needs . . . we are so profoundly ignorant. The exact proportions of the various species of plants, the numbers of each kind of insect or of bird, the peculiarities of more or less exposure to sunshine or to wind at certain critical epochs, and other slight differences which to us are absolutely immaterial and unrecognizable, may be of the highest significance to these humble creatures, and be quite sufficient to require some slight adjustments of size, form, or color, which natural selection will bring about.

In 1906, after reading Gulick's monograph, Henry Edward Crampton decided to enter the fray and to devote the remaining fifty years of his career to an immense study of *Partula* on Tahiti, Moorea, and surrounding islands. Crampton (1875–1956) had done excellent work in experimental embryology and studies of natural selection. This earlier effort led to a slight preference for adaptation, but Crampton maintained an open mind and was prepared to support Gulick's 'internal factors' against Wallace's shaping by environment should the evidence warrant. Crampton made twelve expeditions to the Pacific and published three magnificent monographs – probably the finest work ever done on the evolution of land snails – collectively entitled *Studies on the Variation, Distribution, and Evolution of the Genus* Partula (Tahiti in 1917, other islands in 1925, and Moorea in 1932).

In short, and to summarize a half century of effort in a sentence, Crampton came down firmly on Gulick's side. He could find no evidence that the forms and colors of *Partula* could be predicted from surrounding environments. Identical climatic conditions seemed to evoke different solutions time after time.

Crampton interpreted the differences between snails in adjacent valleys as results of three major causes – isolation, mutation ('congenital factors' in his terminology) and adaptation by natural selection – with only a minor role for Darwin's favorite mechanism. He viewed the first factor, isolation, as a disposing precondition rather than an actual cause: geographic separation produces nothing directly but establishes an independent population in which new features may spread. He saw the third factor, natural selection, as primarily negative. Once new features arise by some other mechanism, natural selection may eliminate them if they prove unworkable – but the source of creative change must lie elsewhere. Crampton, who was one of the first American biologists to recognize the importance of Mendel's work, located this source of creativity in his second factor of mutation, or 'internally generated' change by congenital factors. In any environment, hundreds of possible anatomies might work – and the forms and colors of this particular population in that specific valley are fortuitous consequences of the largely non-adaptive mutations that happened to arise and spread in an isolated population.

The resulting pattern of differences among valleys is largely non-adaptive. Every local race must avoid elimination by natural selection (and is fit in this negative sense), but its particular features represent only one in a myriad of workable possibilities, and any particular solution arises by the happenstance of mutation in an isolated population, not by natural selection. Crampton contrasted the greater importance of mutation over selection in writing about *Partula* on Tahiti:

The role of the environment is to set the limits to the habitable areas or to bring about the elimination of individuals whose qualities are otherwise determined, that is, by congenital factors.

How can we assess the importance of Crampton's work sixty years after his last great monograph on *Partula* from Moorea (1932)? I am biased, to be sure, for snail men (I am one) revere Crampton as a kind of patron saint, but I rank Crampton's *Partula* studies among the most important in the history of evolutionary biology for three major reasons. First, he was probably right in his central claim about the nonadaptive nature of most small-scale differences in form and color among snails of adjacent valleys. Evolutionary biology went through a phase of strong belief in strict adaptationism in the generation just following Crampton, and his works did suffer a temporary eclipse. But his three great monographs are winning new respect and attention in our current, more pluralistic climate of opinion.

Second, Crampton must gain our highest admiration, verging on appropriate awe, for the sheer dedication and effort of his immense labors. I spent only a day in a rented car on Moorea, and scarcely ventured out of the shade or off the paths – but I still nearly passed out from sunstroke. Crampton spent months on twelve separate expeditions, all in an age of ships and horses (not to mention shank's mare), rather than airplanes and rent-a-cars. In the charming understatement of conventional 'objective' scientific prose, Crampton wrote but one small comment on working conditions:

Field-work in such a region of Polynesia presents difficulties that are common to most tropical areas . . . Steamship lines ply between only the principal ports, from which excursions to neighboring islands must be made by cutter, whaleboat, or canoe . . . At times it is possible to procure horses. Almost without exception, however, the exploration of a valley can be accomplished only on foot, owing to the steep declivities to be traversed, the deep streams to be forded, and the absence of any trails whatsoever in the thick forest and undergrowth of the areas inhabited by Partulae.

But Crampton also recorded the countervailing pleasures that keep us all going:

The experiences incidental to the active life necessitated by such work were many, varied, and interesting; but the present monograph is not the place for a description of the beautiful islands or of their delightful inhabitants. Suffice to say that the days and nights of arduous and sometimes dangerous effort included hours of keen enjoyment, for the island of Tahiti, especially, is of matchless beauty, while the chiefs and their families offered abundant hospitalities which it was a privilege to enjoy at the time as it is now a pleasure to acknowledge them.

Moreover, Crampton's labor only began with collecting. He then spent years measuring his snails (some 80,000 for the Tahiti monograph, and a whopping 116,000 for the Moorea work) and calculating statistics – all of which, incredibly (even for his day), he did personally and by hand! (No computers, no hand-held calculators; when Crampton speaks of 'calculating machine', he means those old mechanical jobbies that performed division by successive subtraction and clanked away for minutes to perform simple operations.) Again, he wrote in understatement:

The author is personally responsible for every direct measurement and for every detail of classification; hence the personal coefficient is uniform throughout the entire research ... In computing the standard deviations fractions were carried out to eight decimal places ... The length of time required for such quantitative analysis can be estimated only by those who themselves have engaged in such work ... These figures, together with a single line of text, may be all that represents two to eight weeks of mathematical drudgery ... Yet the employment of such methods is justified in the final results.

Third, and most important, ultimate judgment must reside in a criterion of utility. All good science is accumulative; no one can get everything right the first time. If Crampton's monographs were only monuments to past effort and ideas, they might still be admired, but only as items of human paleontology. They are, in fact, precious mines for continuing revision and extension. I know this in the most personal way, for I have used Crampton's tables, the product of his years of 'mathematical drudgery', in at least three of my technical papers.

To put this crucial point in another and stronger way, Crampton spent fifty years documenting the *current* geographic distribution and variation of *Partula* on Tahiti, Moorea, and nearby islands. This work has great and permanent value as a frozen snapshot, but Crampton's half century should be but a transient moment in the future history of *Partula*. Crampton devoted this lifetime of effort in order to *establish a baseline for future work. Partula* would continue to evolve rapidly, and Crampton's baseline would become a waystation of inestimable value. No scientist could view such dedication in any other light. Future changes have much more value than current impressions.

And Crampton's plan paid off – or so it seemed at first. Three of the world's finest biologists of land snails took up the study of *Partula* in the next generation, building explicitly on Crampton's work – Bryan Clarke of the University of Nottingham, Jim Murray of the University of Virginia, and Mike Johnson of the University of Western Australia. They have published numerous papers, in varying combinations of authorship, from the mid-1960s to the present day. Working primarily on everyone's favorite island of Moorea, they have made important revisions to Crampton's conclusions and have added great sophistication in mathematical procedures (now computerized) and genetical methods not available to Crampton. In 1980, Murray and Clarke ended an important paper, 'The genus *Partula* on Moorea: Speciation in progress', with these words:

Although we cannot yet reconstruct exactly the evolutionary history of the Moorean taxa, they have already revealed in exceptional detail the pattern of interactions between incipient species, and have presented some fascinating paradoxes. They offer both a museum and a laboratory of speciation.

Add snails to Burns' litany about the best laid plans of mice and men. Great expectations die quickly on the bonfires of human vanity. We are only a decade from these brave words of 1980, but Moorea is no longer a laboratory for studying active speciation in *Partula*. It has become a mausoleum.

Think of all the metaphors you know for little things made worse by attempted solutions that cascade to even greater problems, for you need this apparatus to grasp the extirpation of *Partula* on Moorea. Think of Pandora's box. Think of the old 33 woman who swallowed a fly in the folk song. (She then swallowed a spider to catch the fly, a bird to catch the spider, a cat to catch the bird . . . and up the size range of the animal kingdom. Each successive verse gets longer as singers run through the full range of ingestions, but the last is stunningly brief: 'There was an old lady who swallowed a horse. She died, of course.')

Partula eats fungi growing upon dead vegetation and poses no threat whatever to agriculture. Its only, and slight, impact upon the native economy is entirely positive, as women string the shells together to make leis for the tourist trade. But animals introduced onto isolated islands often play havoc both with native organisms and with agriculture, witness the rabbits of Australia and, to cite the most dangerous creature of all, the humans who wiped out so many species of moas on New Zealand. An introduced snail began the sad chain of destruction on Moorea.

In sharp contrast with the benign *Partula*, African tree snails of the genus *Achatina* are, in almost all cases, unmitigated disasters. First of all, they are gigantic (as snails go); second, they are voracious herbivores of living plants, including many agriculturally important species. With their clear record of destruction on island after island, I am amazed that people still introduce them purposefully. (They are brought in for food, for I'm told that they are succulent, and you do get a lot of meat per creature.) *Achatina* was first imported to the Indo–Pacific realm in 1803 by the governor of Réunion who brought them from Madagascar so that a lady friend could continue to enjoy snail soup. They escaped from his garden and devastated the island. By 1847, they had reached India. In the 1930s, they began to spread into South Pacific islands, usually by purposeful introduction for food.

Achatina fulica reached Tahiti in 1967 and soon spread to neighboring islands. By the mid-1970s, the infestation had become particularly serious on Moorea. The snails even invaded human dwellings; one report tells of a farmer who removed two wheelbarrow-loads of *Achatina* from the walls of his house. Admittedly, something had to be done. But *que faire*, as they say in this very French land?

The attempted solution, like the horse ingested to catch the fly, created greater havoc than the original problem. Biological control is a good idea in principle – better a natural predator than a chemical poison. But predators, particularly when introduced from alien places and ecosystems, may engender greater problems than the creature that inspired their introduction. How can you know that the new predator will eat only your problem animal? Suppose it prefers other creatures that are benign or useful? Suppose, in particular, that it attacks endemic species (often so vulnerable for lack of evolved defenses in the absence of native predators)?

Biological control should therefore be attempted only with the utmost caution. But, speaking of folk songs and citing a more recent composition than the old lady and the fly, 'When will they ever learn?' in my personal pantheon of animals to hate and fear, no creature ranks higher than *Euglandina*, the 'killer' or 'cannibal' snail of Florida. *Euglandina* eats other snails – with utmost efficiency and voraciousness. It senses slime trails, locks on to them, and follows the path to a quarry then quickly devoured.

Euglandina has therefore developed a worldwide reputation as a potential agent of biological control for other snails. Yet, despite a few equivocal successes, most attempts have failed, often with disastrous and unintended side-effects, as *Euglandina* leaves the intended enemy alone and turns its attention to a harmless victim.

Forgive my prejudices, but I know what *Euglandina* can do in the most personal way (biologists can get quite emotional about the subjects of their own research). I spent the first big chunk of my career, including my Ph.D. dissertation, working on a remarkable Bermudian land snail named *Poecilozonites*. (This Darwin's finch among mollusks is the only large land snail that reached Bermuda. It radiated into a score of species in a great range of sizes and shapes. The fossil record is particularly rich, but at least three species survived and were thriving in Bermuda when I began my research in 1963.) *Euglandina* had been introduced in 1958 to control *Otala*, an imported edible snail that escaped from a garden and spread throughout the island as an agricultural pest (same story as *Achatina* and *Partula* on Moorea). I don't think that *Euglandina* has even dented *Otala*, but it devastated the native *Poecilozonites*. I used to find them by thousands throughout the island. When I returned in 1973 to locate some populations for a student who wanted to investigate their genetics, I could not find a single animal alive. (Last year, I relocated one species, the smallest and most cryptic, but the large *Poecilozonites bermudensis*, major subject of my research, is probably extinct.)

Thus, I feel the pain of Jim Murray, Bryan Clarke, and Mike Johnson. They had published papers on Moorean *Partula* since the mid-1960s. They never expected that their last pair of articles would be a wake.

Euglandina was introduced to Moorea on March 16, 1977, with the official advice and approval of the *Service de l'Economie Rurale* and the *Division de Recherche Agronomique* – despite
easily available knowledge of its failures and devastations

elsewhere.* *Euglandina* ignored *Achatina* and began a blitzkrieg, against *Partula* – more thorough, rapid, and efficient than anything that Hitler's armies ever accomplished. When my colleagues wrote their first article about this disaster in 1984, *Euglandina* had already wiped out one of the seven *Partula* species on Moorea, and was spreading across the island at a rate of 1.2 km per year. Moorea is about 12 km across at the widest, and you quickly run out of island at that rate. My colleagues made the grim prediction that *Partula* would be completely gone by 1986.

One hates to be right about certain things. In 1988, Jim, Bryan, and Mike published another note with a brief and final title: 'The extinction of *Partula* on Moorea'. *Partula* is gone. My colleagues managed to collect six of the seven species before the end, and they have established captive breeding programs in zoos and biological research stations in several nations. Perhaps,

---

* After this article first appeared in *Natural History*, Bryan Clarke wrote me a letter with the following interesting information on both frustration and hope: 'The story is more depressing than you know. I wrote to the French *Service de l'Economie Rurale* before *Euglandina* was introduced, asking them not to do so. They replied saying that they had not yet decided the matter, but would let me know. Of course they didn't. A similar correspondence took place between Jack Burch at Michigan and the USDA about introducing the Uglies into Hawaii. It got very heated.

There are some little rays of hope. First, it seems that *Euglandina* has not yet reached Huahine, Raiatea or Tahaa, where *Partula* are still, it is said, surviving. I'm going this summer to check. There *may* still be *Partula* on Bora Bora. Second, the French are proposing to set up a snail conservation and study centre on Moorea (shutting the stable door . . .), and we are looking at ways of making "cages" in the woods. There is also a faint hope of a refuge inside the crater of Mehetia (an extinct volcano about 60 miles SE of Tahiti).'

one day, *Partula* can be reintroduced into Moorea. But *Euglandina* must be eliminated first, and no one knows how this can be done. Deep grafts, whether physical or emotional, are hard to extirpate – as Mary Martin discovered in her unsuccessful attempt to wash that man right out of her hair. Hope remains in Pandora's box, but how do you re-enclose the bad guys?

Moorea may be the Bali Ha'i of our dreams, but life for *Partula* has become an unenchanted evening. Now night has fallen.

The story would be sad enough if only Moorea (and Bermuda) had fallen victim. But *Euglandina* is spreading just as rapidly on the larger, adjacent Tahiti, and *Partula* now survives in only two valleys. The even more diverse *Achatinella* is gone (or nearly so) on Oahu, largely for the same reason, although the spread of Honolulu hasn't helped either. More than half the species of bulimulids are extinct on the Galápagos.

It is so hard for an evolutionary biologist to write about extinctions caused by human stupidity. Emotions well up and extinguish rationality in writing. What can be said that hasn't been stated before – with great eloquence and little effect. Even the good arguments have become clichés – as corny as Kansas in August, as normal as blueberry pie.

Let me then float an unconventional plea, the inverse of the usual argument. Inverses often have a salutary effect in reopening pathways of thought. An undergraduate friend during my year in England, a brilliant debater, had to argue the affirmative in that tired old cliché of a subject: 'This house believes that the monarchy should be eliminated'. Instead of trotting out the usual points about the queen's expense account and the negative symbol of royalty in a democratic age, my friend claimed that the monarchy should be eliminated because it is unfair to monarchs and their families. All possibility of a normal private life evaporates. You can't have a date, drink a beer, or, God forbid, even belch in public without a headline in next day's scandal sheet.

The extinction of *Partula* is unfair to *Partula*. This is the conventional argument, and I do not challenge its primacy. But we need a humanistic ecology as well, both for the practical reason that people will always touch people more than snails do or can, and for the moral reason that humans are legitimately the measure of all ethical questions – for these are our issues, not nature's.

So I say, let us grieve for Henry Edward Crampton when we consider *Partula* on Moorea – for *Euglandina* and human stupidity have destroyed his lifetime's dedication. Crampton visited the Pacific a dozen times, when transportation was no aerial picnic. He tramped up and down the valleys, over the dangerous precipices, in intense tropical heat. He spent months and months measuring snails and totting up columns of figures *sans* computer – the worst sort of scientific drudgery. He published three great monographs on *Partula*.

The work is of great and permanent value in itself. But Crampton did not write for personal glory or to establish the frozen evolutionary moment of his own studies. He labored all his life to provide a baseline for future evolutionary work. *Partula* was a natural evolutionary laboratory, and he toiled to establish a starting point, with utmost care and precision, so that others could move the work forward and continue to learn about evolution by tracing the future history of *Partula*. What is more noble than a man's intellectual dedication – a lifetime of perseverance through the Scylla and Charybdis of all field biology: occasional danger and prolonged tedium? Crampton's work is now undone, even mocked. Grieve for his lost and lofty purposes.

Yet I also appreciate that we cannot win this battle to save species and environments without forging an emotional bond between ourselves and nature as well – for we will not fight to save what we do not love (but only appreciate in some abstract sense). So let them all continue – the films, the books, the television programs, the zoos, the little half acre of ecological preserve in any community, the primary school lessons, the museum demonstrations, even (though you will never find me there) the 6:oo a.m. bird walks.

Let them continue and expand because we must have visceral contact in order to love. We really must make room for nature in our hearts. Consider one last image of Ezio Pinza as Emil de Becque in *South Pacific*, and accept the traditional characterization of nature as female (if this convention offends you, then make nature male and fall 'in love with a wonderful guy'). The words may be banal (and Pinza was only extolling Mary Martin, while I speak of all nature), but the emotional setting is incomparable and still can bring tears to any unjaded eye. Think of this greatest of bassos as he soars up to the tonic of his chord:

> Once you have found her, never let her go.
> Once you have found her, NEVER LET HER GO!

Male Nipples and Clitoral Ripples*

The Marquis de Condorcet, enthusiast of the French Revolution but not radical enough for the Jacobins – and therefore forced into hiding from a government that decreed, and would eventually precipitate, his death – wrote in 1793 that 'the perfectibility of man is really boundless ... It has no other limit than the duration of the globe where nature has set us.' As Dickens so aptly remarked, 'It was the best of times, it was the worst of times.'

The very next year, as Condorcet lay dying in prison, a famous voice from across the Channel published another paean to progress in a world that many judged on the brink of ruin. This treatise, called *Zoonomia, or the Laws of Organic Life*, was written by Erasmus Darwin, grandfather of Charles.

Zoonomia is primarily a dissertation on the mechanisms of human physiology. Yet, in the anachronistic tradition that judges biological works by their attitude to the great watershed of evolution, established by grandson Charles in 1859, *Zoonomia*

* The proper and most accurate title of this piece should be 'Tits and Clits' – but such a label would be misread as sexist because people would not recognize the reference point as *male* tits. My wife, a master at titles, suggested this alternative. (During the short heyday of that most unnecessary of all commercially touted products – vaginal deodorants – she wanted to market a male counterpart to be known as 'cocksure'.) *Natural History* magazine, published by a group of fine but slightly overcautious folks, first brought out this essay under their imposed title: 'Freudian Slip'. Not terrible; but not really descriptive either.

owes its modern reputation to a few fleeting passages that look upon organic transmutation with favor.

The evolutionary passages of *Zoonomia* occur in Item 8, Part 4, of Section 39, entitled, 'Of Generation', Erasmus Darwin's thoughts on reproduction and embryology. He viewed embryology as a tale of continuous progress to greater size and complexity. Since his evolutionary speculations are strictly analogous to his concept of embryology, organic transformation also follows a single pathway to more and better:

Would it be too bold to imagine that in the great length of time, since the earth began to exist ... all warm-blooded animals have arisen from one living filament ... possessing the faculty of continuing to improve by its own inherent activity, and of delivering down those improvements by generation to its posterity, world without end?

As the last sentence states, Erasmus Darwin's proposed mechanism of evolution lay in the inheritance of *useful* characters acquired by organisms during their lifetimes. This false theory of heredity has passed through later history under the label of Lamarckism, but the citation by Erasmus (a contemporary of Lamarck) illustrates the extent of this misnomer. Inheritance of acquired characters was the standard folk wisdom of the time, used by Lamarck to be sure, but by no means original or distinctive with him. For Erasmus, this mechanism of evolution required a concept of pervasive utility. New structures arose only when needed and by direct organic striving for an evident purpose. Erasmus discusses adaptations in three great categories: reproduction, protection and defense, and food. Of the last, he writes:

All ... seem to have been gradually produced during many generations by the perpetual endeavor of the creatures to supply the want of food, and to have been delivered to their posterity with constant improvement of them for the purposes required.

In this long section, Erasmus considers only one potential exception to the principle of pervasive utility: 'the breasts and teats of all male quadrupeds, to which no use can be now assigned'. He also suggests two exits from this potential dilemma: first, that male nipples are vestiges of a previous utility if, as Plato had suggested, 'mankind with all other animals were originally hermaphrodites during the infancy of the world, and were in process of time separated into male and female'; and second, that some males may lactate and therefore help to feed their babies (in the absence of any direct evidence, Erasmus cites the milky-colored feeding fluids, produced in the crops of both male and female pigeons, as a possible analogue).

The tenacity of anomalies through centuries of changing beliefs can be truly astounding. As a consequence of writing these essays for so many years, I receive hundreds of letters from readers puzzled about one or another apparent oddity of nature. With so large a sample, I have obtained a pretty good feel for the issues and particulars of evolution that pose conundrums for well-informed non-scientific readers. I have been fascinated (and, I confess, surprised) over the years to discover that no single item has evoked more puzzlement than the very issue that Erasmus Darwin chose as a primary challenge to his concept of pervasive utility – male nipples. I have received more than a dozen requests to explain how evolution could possibly produce such a useless structure.

Consider my latest example from a troubled librarian. 'I have a question that no one can answer for me, and I don't know

where or how to look up the answer. Why do men have nipples?
. . . This question nags at me whenever I see a man's bare chest!'

I was fascinated to note that her two suggestions paralleled exactly the explanations floated by Erasmus Darwin. First, she reports, she asked a doctor. 'He told me that men in primitive societies used to nurse babies.' Finding this incredible, she tried Darwin's first proposal for nipples as a vestige of previous utility: 'Can you tell me – was there once only one sex?'

If you are committed – as Erasmus was, and as a distressingly common version of 'pop', or 'cardboard', Darwinism still is – to a principle of pervasive utility for all parts of all creatures, then male nipples do raise an insoluble dilemma, hence (I assume) my voluminous correspondence. But as with so many persistent puzzles, the resolution does not lie in more research within an established framework but rather in identifying the framework itself as a flawed view of life.

Suppose we begin from a different point of view, focusing on rules of growth and development. The external differences between male and female develop gradually from an early embryo so generalized that its sex cannot be easily determined. The clitoris and penis are one and the same organ, identical in early form, but later enlarged in male fetuses through the action of testosterone. Similarly, the labia majora of women and the scrotal sacs of men are the same structure, indistinguishable in young embryos, but later enlarged, folded over, and fused along the midline in male fetuses.

I do not doubt that the large size and sensitivity of the female breast should count as an adaptation in mammals, but the smaller male version needs no adaptive explanation at all. Males and females are not separate entities, shaped independently by natural selection. Both sexes are variants upon a single ground plan, elaborated in later embryology. Male mammals have nipples because females need them and the embryonic pathway to their development builds precursors in all mammalian fetuses, enlarging the breasts later in females but leaving them small (and without evident function) in males.

In a similar case that illuminates the general principle, the panda develops a highly functional false 'thumb' from the radial sesamoid bone of its wrist. Interestingly, the corresponding bone of the foot, the tibial sesamoid, is also enlarged in the same manner (but not nearly so much), although increase of the tibial sesamoid has no apparent function.

As D. Dwight Davis argued in his great monograph on the giant panda (1964), evolution works on growth fields. Radial and tibial sesamoids are homologous structures, probably affected in concert by the same genetic factors. If natural selection operates for an enlarged radial sesamoid, a bigger tibial sesamoid will probably 'come along for the ride'. Davis drew a profound message from this case: organisms are integral and constrained structures, 'pushing back' against the force of selection to channel changes along permitted paths; complex animals are not a dissociable collection of independent, optimal parts. Davis wrote that 'the effect seen in the sympathetic enlargement of the tibial sesamoid ... strongly suggests that a very simple mechanism, perhaps involving a single factor, lies behind the hypertrophy of the radial sesamoid.'

In my view of life, akin to Davis's concept of constraint and integration, male nipples are an expectation based on pathways of sexual differentiation in mammalian embryology.

At this point, readers might demur with the most crushing of all rejoinders: 'Who cares?' Why worry about little items that ride piggyback on primary adaptations? Let's concentrate on the important thing – the adaptive value of the female breast – and leave aside the insignificant male ornament that arises as its consequence. Adaptations are pre-eminent; their side effects are nooks and crannies of organic design, meaningless bits and pieces. This argument is, I think, the standard position of strict Darwinian adaptationists.

I could defend the importance of structural non-adaptation with a long and abstruse general argument (I have done so in several technical papers). Let me proceed instead by the most compelling route I know by presenting a second example based on human sexuality, a case entirely comparable in concept with the origin of male nipples but differing in importance for human culture – a case, moreover, where the bias of utility has brought needless pain and anxiety into the lives of millions (where, indeed, one might argue that Freudian traditions have provided a manifestly false but potent weapon, however unintentional, for the subjugation of women). Consider the anatomical site of orgasm in human females.

As women have known since the dawn of our time, the primary site for stimulation to orgasm centers upon the clitoris. The revolution unleashed by the Kinsey report of 1953 has, by now, made this information available to men who, for whatever reason, had not figured it out for themselves by the more obvious routes of experience and sensitivity.

The data are unambiguous. Consider only the three most widely read of extensive surveys – the Kinsey report of 1953, Masters and Johnson's book of 1966, and *The Hite Report* of 1976. In his study of genital anatomy, Kinsey reports that the female clitoris is as richly supplied with sensory nerves as the male penis – and therefore as capable of excitation. The walls of the vagina, on the other hand, 'are devoid of end organs of touch and are quite insensitive when they are gently stroked or lightly pressed. For most individuals the insensitivity extends to every part of the vagina.'

The data on masturbation are particularly convincing. Kinsey reports from his sample of 8,000 women that 84 per cent of individuals who have ever masturbated depend 'primarily on labial and/or clitoral techniques'. *The Hite Report* on 3,000 individuals found that 79 per cent of women who masturbate do so by directly stimulating the clitoris and surrounding vulva, while only 1.5 per cent use vaginal entry.

The data on intercourse affirm this pattern. Shere Hite reports a frequency of orgasm with intercourse at 30 per cent and often attained only with simultaneous stimulation of the clitoris by hand. She concludes: '*not* to have orgasm from intercourse is the experience of the majority of women'. Masters and Johnson only included women who experienced orgasm with intercourse in their study. But they concluded that all orgasms are identical in physiology and clitoral in origin. These findings led Hite to comment that human copulation 'sounds more like a Rube Goldberg scheme than a reliable way to orgasm . . . Intercourse was never meant to stimulate women to orgasm.' As Kinsey had said earlier with his characteristic economy and candor: 'The techniques of masturbation and of petting are more specifically calculated to effect orgasm than the techniques of coitus itself.'

This conclusion should be utterly unsurprising – once we grasp the proper role and limitation of adaptationist argument in evolutionary biology. I don't believe in the mystery style of writing essays: build up suspense but save the resolution until the end – for then readers miss the significance of details along the way for want of proper context. The reason for a clitoral site of orgasm is simple – and exactly comparable with the non-puzzle of male nipples. The clitoris is the homologue of the penis – it is the same organ, endowed with the same anatomical organization and capacity of response.

Anatomy, physiology, and observed responses all agree. Why then do we identify an issue at all? Why, in particular, does the existence of clitoral orgasm seem so problematic? Why, for example, did Freud label clitoral orgasm as infantile and define feminine maturity as the shifting to an unattainable vaginal site?

Part of the reason, of course, must reside in simple male vanity. We (and I mean those of my sex, not the vague editorial pronoun) simply cannot abide the idea – though it flows from obvious biology – that a woman's sexual pleasure might not arise most reliably as a direct result of our own coital efforts. But the issue extends further. Clitoral orgasm is a paradox not only for the traditions of Darwinian biology but also for the bias of utility that underlies all functionally based theories of evolution (including Lamarck's and Darwin's) and, in addition, the much older tradition of natural theology that saw God's handiwork in the exquisite fit of organic form to function.

Consider the paradox of clitoral orgasm in any world of strict functionalism (I present a Darwinian version, but parallel arguments can be made for the entire range of functionalist thinking, from Paley's natural theology to Cuvier's creationism): evolution arises from a struggle among organisms for differential reproductive success. Sexual pleasure, in short, must evolve as a stimulus for reproduction.

This formulation works for men since the peak of sexual excitement occurs during ejaculation – a primary and direct adjunct of intercourse. For men, maximal pleasure is linked with the greatest possibility of fathering offspring. In this perspective, the sexual pleasure of women should also be centered upon the act that causes impregnation – on intercourse itself. But how can our world be functional and Darwinian if the site of orgasm is divorced from the place of intercourse? How can sexual pleasure be so separated from its functional significance in the Darwinian game of life? (For the most divergent, but equally functionalist, view of some conservative Christians, sex was made by God to foster procreation; any use in any other context is blasphemy.)

Elisabeth Lloyd, a philosopher of science at Berkeley, has just completed a critical study of explanations recently proposed by evolutionary biologists for the origin and significance of female orgasm. Nearly all these proposals follow the lamentable tradition of speculative storytelling in the *a priori* adaptationist mode. In all the recent Darwinian literature, I believe that Donald Symons is the only scientist who presented what I consider the proper answer – that female orgasm is not an adaptation at all. (See his book, *The Evolution of Human Sexuality*, 1979.)

Many of these scientists don't even know the simple facts of the matter; they assume that female orgasms are triggered by intercourse and draw the obvious Darwinian conclusion. A second group recognizes the supposed paradox of non-association between orgasm and intercourse and then proposes another sort of adaptive explanation, usually based on maintenance of the pair bond by fostering close relationships through sexual pleasure. Desmond Morris (*The Naked Ape*, 1969), the most widely read promoter of this view, writes that female orgasm evolved for its role in promoting the pair bond by 'the immense behavioral reward it brings to the act of sexual cooperation with the mated partner'. Perhaps no popular speculation has been more androcentric than George Pugh's (*Biological Origin of Human Values*, 1977), who speaks about 'the development of a female orgasm, which makes it easier for a female to be satisfied by one 49 male, and which also operates psychologically to produce a stronger emotional bond in the female'. Or Eibl-Eibesfeldt, who argues (1975) that the evolution of female orgasm 'increases her readiness to submit and, in addition, strengthens her emotional bond to the partner'.

This popular speculation about pair bonding usually rests upon an additional biological assumption – almost surely false – that capacity for female orgasm is an especially human trait. Yet Symons shows, in his admirable review of the literature, that whereas most female mammals do not experience orgasm during ordinary copulation, prolonged clitoral stimulation – either artificially in the laboratory (however unpleasant a context from the human point of view) or in nature by rubbing against another animal (often a female) – does produce orgasm in a wide range of mammals, including many primates. Symons concludes that 'orgasm is most parsimoniously interpreted as a potential all female mammals possess'.

Adaptive stories for female orgasm run the full gamut – leaving only the assumption of adaptation itself unquestioned. Sarah Hrdy (1981), for example, has taken up the cudgels against androcentrism in evolutionary speculation, not by branding the entire enterprise as bankrupt, but by showing that she can tell just as good an adaptive story from a female-centered point of view. She argues – turning the old pair-bond theory on its head – that the dissociation between orgasm and intercourse is an adaptation for promiscuous behavior, permitting females to enlist the support of several males to prevent any one from harming her babies. (In many species, a male that displaces a female's previous partner may kill her offspring, presumably to foster his own reproductive success by immediate remating.)

Indeed, no one surpasses Hrdy in commitment to the adaptationist assumption that orgasm must have evolved for Darwinian utility in promoting reproductive success. Chosen language so often gives away an underlying bias; note Hrdy's equation of non-adaptation both with despair in general and with the denigration of women's sexuality in particular.

Are we to assume, then, that [the clitoris] is irrelevant? . . . It would be safer to suspect that, like most organs . . . it serves a purpose, or once did . . . The lack of obvious purpose has left the way open for both orgasm, and female sexuality in general, to be dismissed as 'non-adaptive'.

But why are adaptationist arguments 'safe', and why is non-adaptation a 'dismissal'? I do not feel degraded because my nipples are concomitants of a general pattern in human development and not a sign that ancestors of my sex once lactated. In fact, I find this non-adaptationist explanation particularly fascinating, both because it teaches me something important about structural rules of development and because it counters a pervasive and constraining bias that has harmed evolutionary biology by restricting the range of permitted hypotheses. Why should the dissociation of orgasm from intercourse degrade women when it merely records a basic (if unappreciated) fact of human anatomy that happens to unite both sexes as variations of a common pattern in development? (Such an argument would only hold if adaptations were 'good' and all other aspects of anatomy 'irrelevant'. I, for one, am quite attached to all my body parts and do not make such invidious rankings and distinctions among them.)

I could go on but will stop here for the obvious reason that this discussion, however amusing, might be deemed devoid of social importance. After all, these biologists may be enjoying themselves and promoting their view of life, but isn't all this strictly *entre nous*? I mean, after all, who cares about speculative ideas if they impose no palpable harm upon people's lives? But, unfortunately, the history of psychology shows that one of the most influential theories of our century – a notion that had a direct and deeply negative effect upon millions of women – and rested upon the false assumption that clitoral orgasm cannot be the natural way of a mature female. I speak, of course, about Sigmund Freud's theory of transfer from clitoral to vaginal orgasm.

In Freud's landmark and most influential book, *Three Essays on the Theory of Sexuality* (1905, but first published in complete form in 1915), the third essay on 'transformations of puberty' argues that 'the leading erotogenic zone in female children is located at the clitoris'. He also, as a scientist originally trained in anatomy, knows the reason – that the clitoris 'is homologous to the masculine genital zone of the glans penis'.

Freud continues: 'All my experience concerning masturbation in little girls has related to the clitoris and not the regions of the external genitalia that are important in later sexual functioning.' So far so good; Freud recognizes the phenomenon, knows its anatomical basis, and should therefore identify clitoral orgasm as a proper biological expression of female sexuality. Not at all, for Freud then describes a supposed transformation in puberty that defines the sexuality of mature women.

Puberty enhances the libido of boys but produces an opposite effect in girls – 'a fresh wave of repression'. Later, sexuality resumes in a new way. Freud writes:

When at last the sexual act is permitted and the clitoris itself becomes excited, it still retains a function: the task, namely, of transmitting the excitation to the adjacent female sexual parts, just as – to use a simile –

pine shavings can be kindled in order to set a log of harder wood on fire.

Thus, we encounter Freud's famous theory of female sexual maturity as a transfer from clitoral to vaginal orgasm:

When erotogenic susceptibility to stimulation has been successfully transferred by a woman from the clitoris to the vaginal orifice, it implies that she has adopted a new leading zone for the purposes of her later sexual activity.

This dogma of transfer from clitoral to vaginal orgasm became a shibboleth of pop culture during the heady days of pervasive Freudianism. It shaped the expectations (and therefore the frustration and often misery) of millions of educated and 'enlightened' women told by a brigade of psychoanalysts and by hundreds of articles in magazines and 'marriage manuals' that they must make this biologically impossible transition as a definition of maturity.

Freud's unbiological theory did further harm in two additional ways. First, Freud did not define frigidity only as an inability to perform sexually or as inefficacy in performance, but proposed as his primary definition a failure to produce this key transfer from clitoris to vagina. Thus, a woman who greatly enjoys sex, but only by clitoral stimulation, is frigid by Freud's terminology. 'This anaesthesia,' Freud writes, 'may become permanent if the clitoridal zone refuses to abandon its excitability.'

Second, Freud attributed a supposedly greater incidence of neurosis and hysteria in women to the difficulty of this transfer – for men simply retain their sexual zone intact from childhood, while women must undergo the hazardous switch from clitoris to vagina. Freud continues:

The fact that women change their leading erotogenic zone in this way, 53 together with the wave of repression at puberty ... are the chief determinants of the greater proneness of women to neurosis and especially to hysteria. These determinants, therefore, are intimately related to the essence of femininity.

In short, Freud's error may be encapsulated by stating that he defined the ordinary biology of female sexuality as an aberration based on failure to abandon an infantile tendency.

The sources of Freud's peculiar theory are complex and involve many issues not treated in this essay (in particular his androcentric biases in interpreting the act of intercourse from a man's point of view and in defining both clitoral and penile stimulation in childhood as a fundamentally masculine form of sexuality that must be shunned by a mature woman). But another important source resides in the perspective underlying all the fanciful theories that I have discussed throughout this essay, from male nipples as sources of milk to clitoral orgasm as a clever invention to cement pair bonds – the bias of utility, or the exclusive commitment to functionalist explanations.

The more I read Kinsey, the more he wins my respect for his humane sensibility, and for his simple courage. (His 1953 report on *Sexual Behavior in the Human Female* appeared during the height of McCarthyism in America and led to a withdrawal of funding for his research and the effective end, during his lifetime, of his programs – see the essay 'Of Wasps and WASPs' in my previous book, *The Flamingo's Smile*.) Kinsey was a measured man. He wrote in a dry and clinical fashion (probably more for reasons of necessity than inclinations of temperament). Yet, every once in a while, his passion spills forth and his rage erupts in a single, well-controlled phrase. Nowhere does Kinsey express more agitation than in his commentary on Freud's theory of the shift from clitoral to vaginal orgasm.

Kinsey locates his discussion of Freud in the proper context – in his section on sexual anatomy (Chapter 14, 'Anatomy of Sexual Response and Orgasm'). He reports the hard data on adult masturbation and on the continuing clitoral site of orgasm in mature women. He locates the reason for clitoral orgasm not in any speculative theory about function but in the basic structure of sexual anatomy.

In any consideration of the functions of the adult genitalia, and especially of their liability to sensory stimulation, it is important and imperative that one take into account the homologous origins of the structures in the two sexes.

Kinsey then provides a long and beautifully clear discussion of anatomical homologies, particularly the key unity of penis and clitoris. He concludes that 'the vaginal walls are quite insensitive in the great majority of females . . . There is no evidence that the vagina is ever the sole source of arousal, or even the primary source of erotic arousal in any female.' Kinsey has now laid the foundation for a swift demolition of Freud's hurtful theory. He cites (in a long footnote, for his text is not contentious) a compendium of psychoanalytical proclamations from the Freudian heyday of the 1920s to 1940s. Consider just three items on his list:

1. (from 1936): 'If this transition [from clitoris to vagina] is not successful, then the woman cannot experience satisfaction in the sexual act . . . The first and decisive requisite of a normal orgasm is vaginal sensitivity.'

2. (again from 1936): 'The sole criterion of frigidity is the absence of the vaginal orgasm.'

3. (from 1927): 'In frigidity the pleasurable sensation is as a rule situated in the clitoris and the vaginal zone has none.'

Kinsey's sole paragraph of evaluation ranks as the finest dismissal by understatement (and by incisive phrase at the end) that I have ever read.

This question is one of considerable importance because much of the literature and many of the clinicians, including psychoanalysts and some of the clinical psychologists and marriage counselors, have expended considerable effort trying to teach their patients to transfer 'clitoral responses' into 'vaginal responses'. Some hundreds of women in our own study and many thousands of the patients of certain clinicians have consequently been much disturbed by their failure to accomplish this biological impossibility.

I then must ask myself, why could Kinsey be so direct and sensible in 1953, while virtually all evolutionary discussion of female orgasm during the past twenty years has been not only biologically erroneous but also obtuse and purely speculative? I'm sorry to convert this essay into something of a broken record in contentious repetition, but the same point pervades the discussion all the way from Erasmus Darwin on male nipples to Sarah Hrdy on clitoral orgasm. The fault lies in a severely restrictive (and often false) functionalist view of life. Most functionalists have not misinterpreted male nipples, for their unobtrusive existence poses no challenge. But clitoral orgasm is too central to the essence of life for any explanation that does not focus upon the role of sexuality in reproductive success. And yet the obvious, non-adaptive structural alternative stares us in the face as the most elementary fact of sexual anatomy – the homology of penis and clitoris.

Kinsey's ability to cut through this morass right to the core of the strong developmental argument has interesting roots. Kinsey began his career by devoting twenty years to the taxonomy of gall-forming wasps. He pursued this work in the 1920s and

1930s before American evolutionary biology congealed around Darwinian functionalism. In Kinsey's day, many (probably most) taxonomists accepted the non-adaptive nature of much small-scale geographic variability within species. Kinsey followed this structuralist tradition and never absorbed the bias of utility. He was therefore able to grasp the meaning of this elemental fact of homology between penis and clitoris – a fact that stares everyone in the face, but becomes invisible if the bias of utility be strong enough.

I well remember something that Francis Crick said to me many years ago, when my own functionalist biases were strong. He remarked, in response to an adaptive story I had invented with alacrity and agility to explain the meaning of repetitive DNA: 'Why do you evolutionists always try to identify the value of something before you know how it is made?' At the time, I dismissed this comment as the unthinking response of a hide-bound molecular reductionist who did not understand that evolu-tionists must always seek the 'why' as well as the 'how' – the final as well as the efficient causes of structures.

Now, having wrestled with the question of adaptation for many years, I understand the wisdom of Crick's remark. If all structures had a 'why' framed in terms of adaptation, then my original dismissal would be justified for we would know that 'whys' exist whether or not we had elucidated the 'how'. But I am now convinced that many structures (including male nipples and clitoral orgasm) have no direct adaptational 'why'. And we discover this by studying pathways of genetics and development – or, as Crick so rightly said to me, by first understanding how a structure is built. In other words, we must first establish 'how' in order to know whether or not we should be asking 'why' at all.

I began with Charles Darwin's grandpa Erasmus and end with his namesake, Desiderius Erasmus, the greatest of all Renaissance scholars. Of more than 3,000 proverbs from antiquity collected in his *Adagia* of 1508, perhaps two are best known and wonderfully apt for the point of this essay (which is not a diatribe against adaptation but a plea for expansion by alternative hypotheses and for fruitful competition and synthesis between functional and structural perspectives). First a comment on limitations of outlook: 'No one is injured save by himself.' Second, probably the most famous of zoological metaphors about human temperament: 'The fox has many tricks, and the hedgehog only one, but that is the best of all.' Some have taken the hedgehog's part in this dichotomy, but I will cast my lot for a diversity of options – for our complex world may offer many paths to salvation, and the hounds of hell press continually upon us.

READ MORE IN PENGUIN

For complete information about books available from Penguin and how to order them, please write to us at the appropriate address below. Please note that for copyright reasons the selection of books varies from country to country.

IN THE UNITED KINGDOM: Please write to *Dept. JC, Penguin Books Ltd, FREEPOST, West Drayton, Middlesex UB7 0BR.*
If you have any difficulty in obtaining a title, please send your order with the correct money, plus ten per cent for postage and packaging, to *PO Box No. 11, West Drayton, Middlesex UB7 0BR.*

IN THE UNITED STATES: Please write to *Consumer Sales, Penguin USA, P.O. Box 999, Dept. 17109, Bergenfield, New Jersey 07621-0120.* VISA and MasterCard holders call 1-800-253-6476 to order all Penguin titles.

IN CANADA: Please write to *Penguin Books Canada Ltd, 10 Alcorn Avenue, Suite 300, Toronto, Ontario M4V 3B2.*

IN AUSTRALIA: Please write to *Penguin Books Australia Ltd, P.O. Box 257, Ringwood, Victoria 3134.*

IN NEW ZEALAND: Please write to *Penguin Books (NZ) Ltd, Private Bag 102902, North Shore Mail Centre, Auckland 10.*

IN INDIA: Please write to *Penguin Books India Pvt Ltd, 706 Eros Apartments, 56 Nehru Place, New Delhi 110 019.*

IN THE NETHERLANDS: Please write to *Penguin Books Netherlands bv, Postbus 3507, NL-1001 AH Amsterdam.*

IN GERMANY: Please write to *Penguin Books Deutschland GmbH, Metzlerstrasse 26, 60594 Frankfurt am Main.*

IN SPAIN: Please write to *Penguin Books S. A., Bravo Murillo 19, 1o B, 28015 Madrid.*

IN ITALY: Please write to *Penguin Italia s.r.l., Via Felice Casati 20, I-20124 Milano.*

IN FRANCE: Please write to *Penguin France S. A., 17 rue Lejeune, F-31000 Toulouse.*

IN JAPAN: Please write to *Penguin Books Japan, Ishikiribashi Building, 2-5-4, Suido, Bunkyo-ku, Tokyo 112.*

IN GREECE: Please write to *Penguin Hellas Ltd, Dimocritou 3, GR-106 71 Athens.*

IN SOUTH AFRICA: Please write to *Longman Penguin Southern Africa (Pty) Ltd, Private Bag X08, Bertsham 2013.*